First published in Great Britain in 2020 by Egmont UK Limited
2 Minster Court, 10th floor, London EC3R 7BB
www.egmont.co.uk

Editorial and design by Cloud King Creative

ISBN 978 1 4052 9930 5
71202/001
Printed in Great Britain

# PRESENT DANGER

In a future world, peace is threatened by an evil computer virus trapped in a cyber dimension. Evox is set on taking over the source of all the Rangers' power — the Morphin Grid itself — and defeating the Power Rangers for good! Earth's only hope is the team of Power Rangers known as the Beast Morphers. **Will they succeed?**

Can you help the Power Rangers take on Evox and his evil henchmen? You'll need patience, strength and courage to solve the puzzles that stand in your way. Fail and you risk Evox stealing the Morph-X he needs to acquire a real body and become all-powerful!

# GO GO! POWER RANGERS

# ZORD ORDER

Zords are the giant mechanical vehicles that the Rangers sometimes pilot to help them fight the good fight. Turn the word 'ZORD' into 'GOOD' by changing one letter at a time to make a new word, without rearranging any of the letters. For example, you *could* change ZORD to LORD ... but it wouldn't be right! Use the clues to help you.

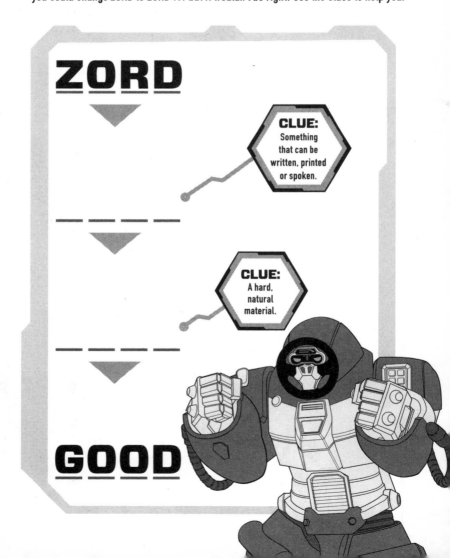

**ZORD**

CLUE:
Something that can be written, printed or spoken.

_ _ _ _

CLUE:
A hard, natural material.

_ _ _ _

**GOOD**

6

# REAL RANGER

Evil Evox has created clones of Roxy! Only one Yellow Ranger below is the real one — she matches the big picture. Study the picture, then cross out the four fake Rangers below.

A

B

C

D

E

# HERO HACKER

Help computer ace Devon hack the grid to stop Evox. Start at the letter A, then follow a path through the grid in order of the alphabet.

|   | A | B | C | E | G | P |
|---|---|---|---|---|---|---|
|   | B | F | G | S | W | I |
| F | D | C | N | O | T | U | W |
| B | E | A | M | P | S | V | Y |
| H | F | G | L | Q | R | W | V |
| I | C | H | K | M | Y | X | Q |
| J | F | I | J | N | Z |   |   |
| K | L | N | M | O | X |   |   |

# STRANGE RIDDLE

DIFFICULTY:

The Rangers need your help to solve a mysterious riddle. Can you work out the letters that spell out the word?

My first letter is in **REBEL** and also in **ROCK,**

My second letter is in **SOAR** but never in **SCORE,**

My third letter is in **NATE** and also in **NIGHT,**

My fourth letter is in **RING** but never in **RITE,**

My fifth letter is in **TEAM** but never in **MATT,**

My sixth letter is in **RUMBLE** but never in **TUMBLE,**

My last letter is in **STAR** and also in **SNOW.**

When you've solved the riddle, write the word below:

# POWERFUL PARTNERS

The Power Rangers have robotic partners called Beast Bots. They answer the call whenever the Rangers need them. Connect each Ranger with their Beast Bot, then match each Bot to its special skill.

RED

*Powerful jumping and kicking.*

BLUE

*The super speed of a cheetah.*

YELLOW

*Incredible physical strength.*

## Quick Count

*How many times can you see the word DNA in the letter grid? Count the times you can see the word spelled forwards, backwards, up or down only.*

| D | N | A | N |
|---|---|---|---|
| N | A | N | D |
| A | N | D | N |
| D | N | A | A |

_____ times

# BATTLE SCARS

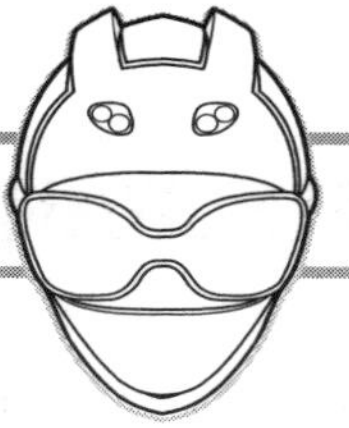

The Yellow Ranger has had a narrow escape in a battle with Blaze's clone! Help her put the pieces of her helmet back together by writing the letters in the spaces below.

**Warning!** One piece doesn't fit, circle the piece you don't need.

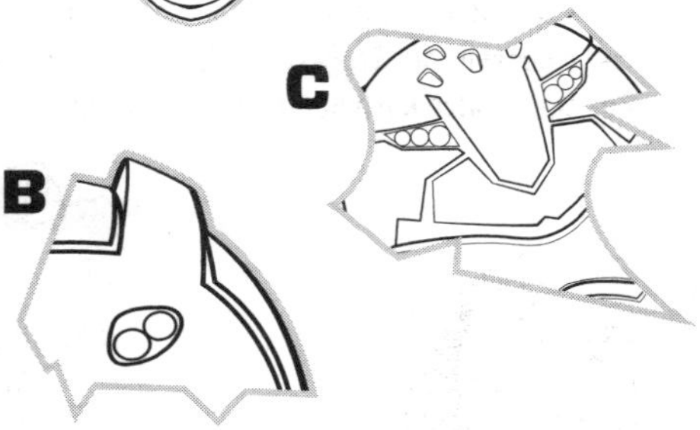

C

B

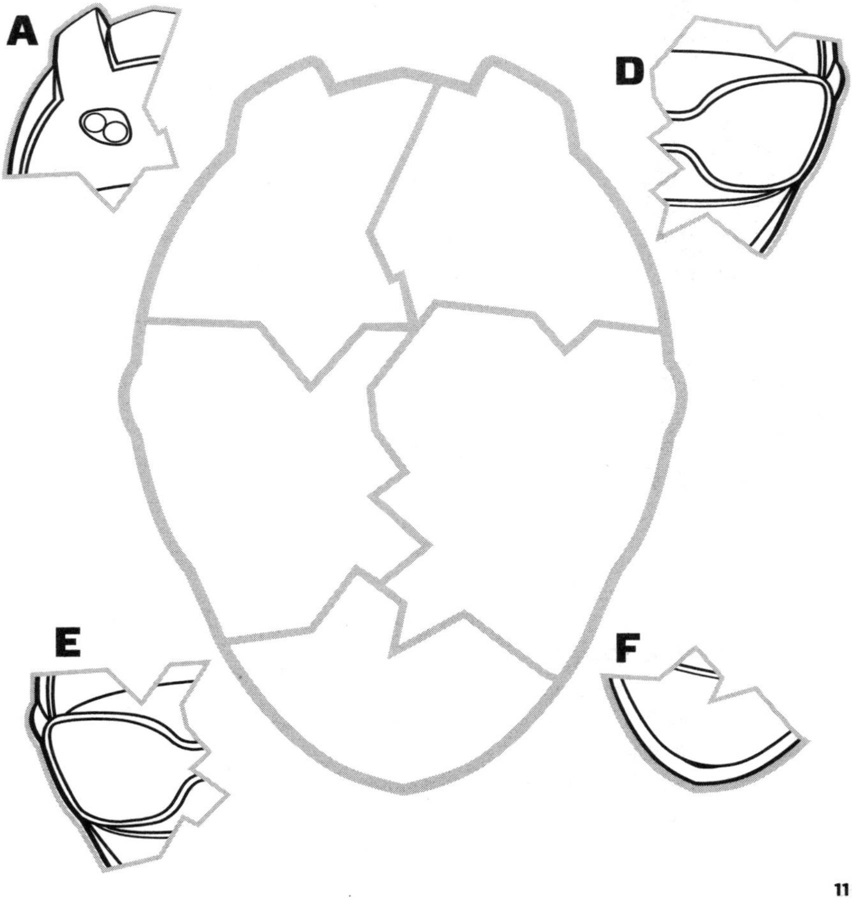

A

D

E

F

# MIRROR MESSAGE

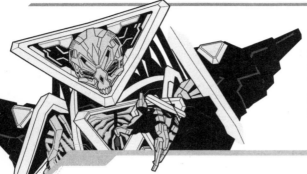

The Power Rangers' next destination has been scrambled by a virus. Can you work out what it says? Use a mirror if you get stuck.

**THE POWER RANGERS MUST TRAVEL INTO THE CYBER DIMENSION TO DEFEAT EVOX.**

**ANSWER:** _____

_____

_____

_____

# MORPHIN MISSION

Commander Shaw has chosen two Rangers for a mission to keep the Morphin Grid safe. Follow the lines to work out who, then copy their helmets into the spaces.

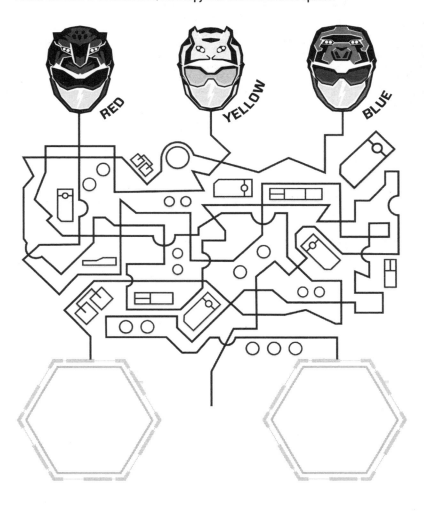

RED

YELLOW

BLUE

**RANGER**          **RANGER**

13

# TEAM TEST

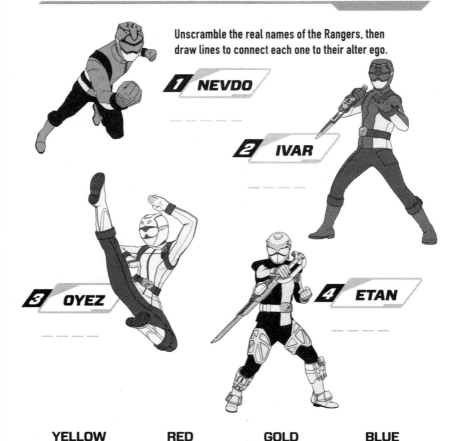

Unscramble the real names of the Rangers, then draw lines to connect each one to their alter ego.

**1** NEVDO

**2** IVAR

**3** OYEZ

**4** ETAN

YELLOW        RED        GOLD        BLUE

## Quick Quiz

*Now try to answer these questions about the Rangers.*

**1.** Which Ranger's Zord has a jackrabbit mode? _ _ _ _

**2.** Whose fists can transform into Cheetah Claws? _ _ _ _ _

**3.** The drive blade belongs to which Power Ranger? _ _ _ _

**4.** Who is the owner of a binocular blade? _ _ _ _

# SMASH AND GRAB

Join the dots to meet Ravi's
battling Beast Bot.

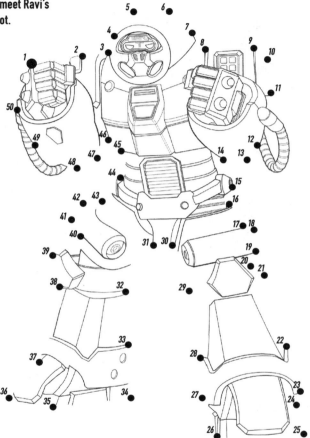

## Name That Mecha
Unscramble the letters to reveal
the name of the Beast.

# ON THE ROX

Roxy was infected by Evox's evil virus and became one of his Generals. Try to help Roxy switch back to the good side by placing the letters R, O, X and Y once in every row, column and 2x2 box.

## Puzzle 1: Easy

| Y | X |   |   |
|---|---|---|---|
| R | O | X |   |
|   |   | O |   |
| O | R |   |   |

## Puzzle 2: Medium

|   | O | Y |   |
|---|---|---|---|
| X |   |   |   |
|   |   | O |   |
|   | R | X |   |

16

# BUILDING A BROTHER

DIFFICULTY:

Nate built Steel the Silver Ranger hoping he'd be like a real brother. Only one of these robots is the final version of Steel — the others are still being built. Circle the finished Silver Ranger.

# EVOX'S EVOLUTION

With each Morph-X upgrade, Evox gains the energy he needs to create a physical form. His avatar still needs some work — can you piece Evox together in the correct order? Number 1 has been filled in for you.

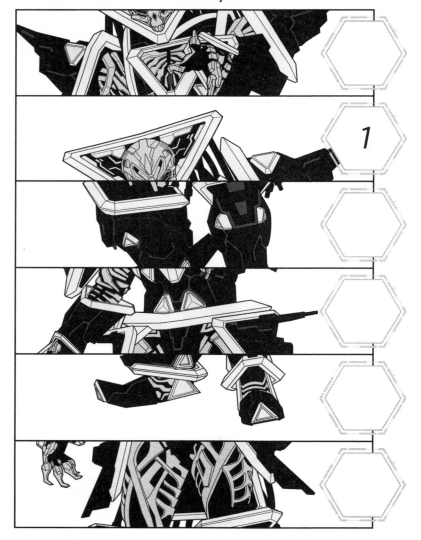

# MECHA MAZE

Starting at number 1, fill in the missing numbers in order from 1–20, then trace a path for the Megazord to track down Evox's henchmen at Coral Harbour. You can go up, down, forwards or backwards, but not diagonally.

Example solution:

| 8 | 7 | 4 | 3 |
|---|---|---|---|
| 9 | 6 | 5 | 2 |
| 10 | 13 | 14 | 1 |
| 11 | 12 | 15 | 16 |

| 5 | 10 | | 10 | 19 |
|---|---|---|---|---|
| 6 | 7 | 8 | 11 | 20 |
| | 4 | | 12 | 19 |
| 2 | 3 | 14 | 13 | 18 |
| 1 | 5 | 15 | | 17 |

CORAL HARBOUR

# GOING VIRAL

Which viral villain is powering up?
Rearrange the picture to reveal the answer.

# VILE VILLAINS

Nine crafty criminals are hiding in this grid. Their names are written either forwards or backwards and in any direction — including diagonally. How many can you track down?

| S | C | I | N | O | R | T | F | T | X | S | W | D | H | V |
|---|---|---|---|---|---|---|---|---|---|---|---|---|---|---|
| J | N | B | Z | X | M | O | A | G | C | N | P | R | A | W |
| M | T | M | U | O | U | N | B | I | C | E | A | R | X | Z |
| V | N | E | L | V | Q | D | N | O | W | V | G | M | D | U |
| M | L | V | Z | E | D | O | N | Y | T | O | K | T | A | B |
| L | W | L | Q | A | R | J | X | O | Y | R | D | S | X | Y |
| K | Y | M | O | T | L | O | M | L | D | Y | O | D | A | W |
| Z | R | X | A | B | R | B | E | B | S | F | A | N | Q | S |
| A | O | G | I | G | A | D | R | O | N | E | S | O | S | C |
| M | I | H | N | O | I | L | J | P | U | Q | F | W | M | R |
| G | C | H | N | L | X | F | Y | R | Y | C | O | E | J | O |
| H | W | Z | D | T | L | P | U | Q | M | P | P | Y | P | Z |
| P | X | N | Q | G | P | M | Z | W | A | N | X | V | B | Z |
| Y | K | O | L | I | A | T | G | C | C | O | Y | X | G | L |
| L | F | K | D | A | K | I | D | B | E | O | Y | B | E | E |

| BLAZE | EVOX | GIGADRONES |
|---|---|---|
| GIGATRONICS | ROBOTRONS | ROXY |
| SCROZZLE | TRONICS | VARGOYLE |

# TIMED TEASER

**DIFFICULTY:**

Begin at the start and trace a path passing only through the Rangers and avoiding Evox and his evil crew. Sound easy? Try to reach the finish in under 30 seconds.

**START**

| TRONICS | EVOX | RED |

| CYBER BLAZE | BLUE | VARGOYLE |

| GOLD | SILVER | CYBER ROXY |

| YELLOW | SCROZZLE | ROBOTRONS |

**FINISH**

# RADAR REVEAL

The Rangers are checking their radar for enemy activity. Can you write down the coordinates to show where each villain is hiding? The first one has been done for you.

| | A | B | C | D | E | F | G |
|---|---|---|---|---|---|---|---|
| 7 | | | | | villain | | |
| 6 | | | villain | | | | |
| 5 | | | | | | | villain |
| 4 | | | villain | | | | |
| 3 | | | | | villain | | |
| 2 | | | | | | | |
| 1 | villain | | | | | | |

**ROXY** _C6_        **TRONICS** ___ ___

**BLAZE** ___ ___

**EVOX** ___ ___

23

# TRIPLE TEST

Power Rangers must possess excellent powers of observation.
Count the different Rangers' helmets and write down the totals.

RED

YELLOW

BLUE

## *Hidden Enemy*
*Which villain is hiding in the helmets?*
*Write their name below.*

# OFF GRID

While the Power Rangers' enemies are lying low, our heroes remain on high alert.
Place all of the enemies into the grid once, so that they read either across or down.

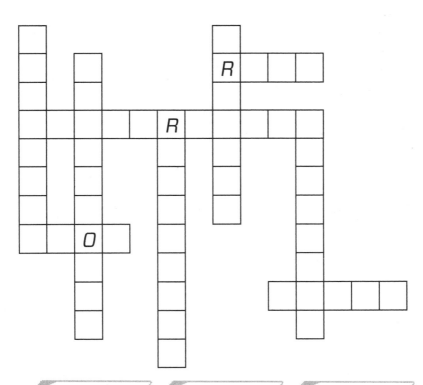

| 4-LETTER WORDS | 5-LETTER WORD | 7-LETTER WORD |
|---|---|---|
| EVOX | BLAZE | TRONICS |
| ROXY | | |

| 8-LETTER WORDS | 9-LETTER WORD |
|---|---|
| VARGOYLE | ROBOTRONS |
| SCROZZLE | |

| 10-LETTER WORD | 11-LETTER WORD |
|---|---|
| GIGADRONES | GIGATRONICS |

# TOUGH WORKOUT

The real Blaze loves his karate lessons at Riptide Gym. After his sessions he needs an energy-boosting snack. Use the code to help you work out the prices of the snacks. The price of a shake has been done for you.

| A | B | C | D | E | F | G | H | I | J | K | L | M |
|---|---|---|---|---|---|---|---|---|---|---|---|---|
| 1 | 2 | 1 | 5 | 2 | 4 | 1 | 5 | 1 | 4 | 1 | 2 | 3 |

| N | O | P | Q | R | S | T | U | V | W | X | Y | Z |
|---|---|---|---|---|---|---|---|---|---|---|---|---|
| 3 | 1 | 2 | 5 | 1 | 2 | 2 | 1 | 4 | 3 | 1 | 5 | 4 |

**SHAKE**

**$11**

**SHAKE:** 2 + 5 + 1 + 1 + 2 = 11

**SOUP**

$ _ _ _ _ _

**CARROTS**

$ _ _ _ _ _

**BANANA**

$ _ _ _ _ _

RIPTIDE
— G Y M —

Evox's evil virus has spread to Zoey's computer. What's wrong with this picture? Circle eight things that have changed from the original shot.

# RANGER CODE

Devon has important instructions for his fellow Rangers, but he has written his message in code so that Evox won't know his next move. Scribble out the letter X every time it appears to reveal Devon's mystery message.

XXSTXAXNXDBXAXCXKX

XIXXMXGXOXNXNXA

XMXOXRXPXHX!

# PINCER MOVEMENT

The Silver Ranger's Zord is in Stag Beetle mode, ready to scuttle into battle. Trace over the lines to complete the mighty Zord.

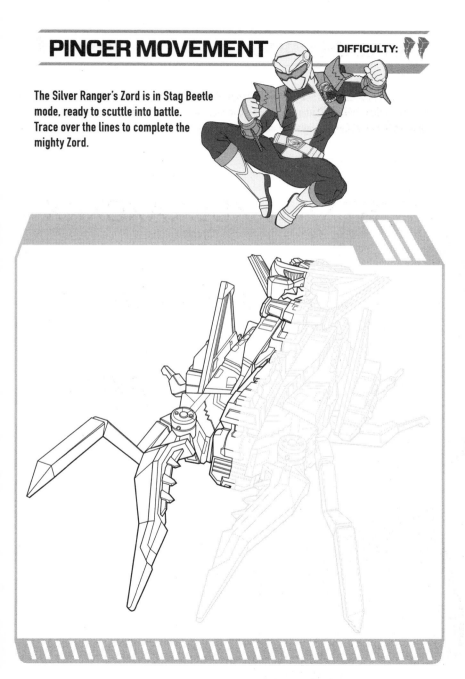

# TARGET PRACTICE

The Silver Ranger is an expert with a blaster. Help him practise some sharp shooting by hitting one number in the outer ring, one number in the middle ring and one number in the inner ring each time. These three numbers must add up to the correct total.

For example, to score 26 you would blast the 5 in the outer ring, the 11 in the middle ring and the 10 in the inner ring, as $5 + 11 + 10 = 26$.

*Totals to score:*

_____ + _____ + _____ = **18**

_____ + _____ + _____ = **21**

_____ + _____ + _____ = **41**

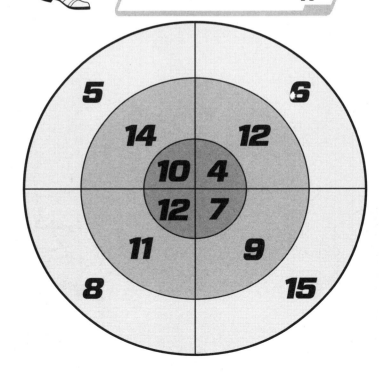

# DEFENDERS OF THE GRID

The Power Rangers will defend to the end! Study the picture and see if you can spot eight hidden lightning bolts.

# SCROZZLE'S SERVANTS

Scrozzle creates these mystery monsters from ordinary objects, but do you know what they are called?

Trace a path in straight lines to find the nine-letter name hidden in the grid below. Diagonals are not allowed. How many five letter words can you spell?

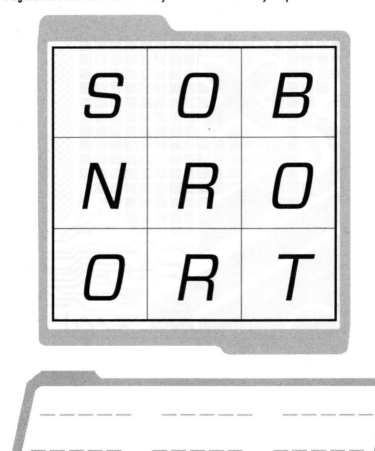

# FORCE FOR GOOD

Colour in the shapes using the colour code to reveal a team of Rangers, ready to tackle any enemy.

**1** = red      **2** = blue      **3** = yellow      **4** = grey

**Which Rangers?** Tick the Rangers that make up the trio above.

SILVER ☐     RED ☐     BLUE ☐     GOLD ☐     YELLOW ☐

# ZORD LAUNCH

**DIFFICULTY:**

The Blue Ranger's Zord is ready for action. Work out which picture panels are missing from the main picture, then try drawing in the missing pieces.

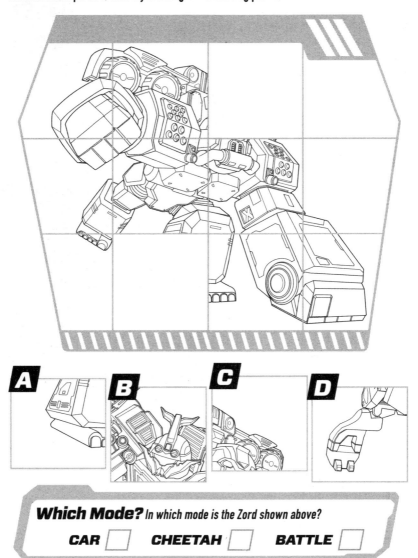

**A**

**B**

**C**

**D**

***Which Mode?*** *In which mode is the Zord shown above?*

**CAR** ☐     **CHEETAH** ☐     **BATTLE** ☐

# ULTRA DEFENCE

When things get serious, all five Rangers combine
to pilot the Ultrazord in their individual cockpits.

Complete the grid below so that each
colour Ranger appears once, for
example RED. The names read
either down or across.

E

O

# OUT OF SEQUENCE

**DIFFICULTY:**

One item is missing from each sequence. Work out the pattern, then draw the item that's missing from each row.

**1**

**2**

**3**

**4**

# RELEASE THE BEASTS!

DIFFICULTY:

Fill in the missing letters to complete the mode for each Zord.

**CLUE:** The modes are all named after animals.

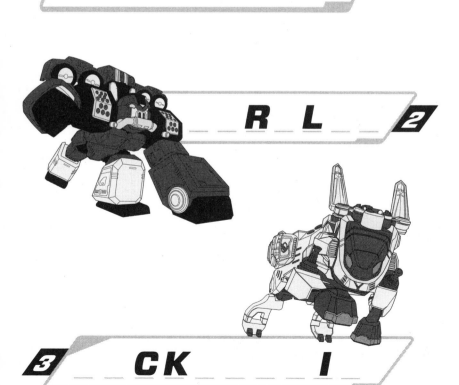

**1** _ _ _ A G _ E T _ _ _

**2** _ _ R _ L _ _

**3** _ _ _ C K _ _ _ I _

# BLADE BUILDER

Nate is building some new blades for the Rangers team. He has already built his own prototype, shown above. Now he must use the rest of the material to build identical blades for each of the four Rangers — Blue, Red, Yellow and Silver.

Each piece must be <u>exactly</u> the same shape. While they can be rotated, they cannot be flipped over. All of the material must be used, without any squares left over. Draw lines to make four identical blades.

# CYBER SERVANT

Once a Ranger in training, this soldier now sides with Evox.
Join the dots to reveal the evil general.

# SIXTH SENSE

Can you make sense of this puzzle?
Which letter should replace the question
mark below? Try to solve the puzzle in
under three minutes to beat the speedy
Red Ranger's record!

L O

? E

W L

# TRI AGAIN

DIFFICULTY:

Nate Silva is the Rangers' chief problem-solver — there's no puzzle he can't crack.
Try your hand at this brainteaser. How many triangles appear below?

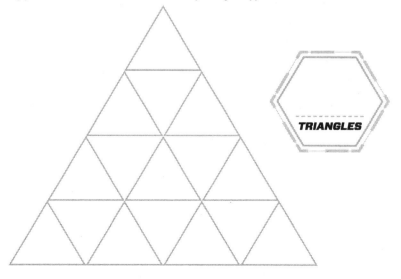

TRIANGLES

# HAVING A BLAST

Animal-lover Zoey was fused with jackrabbit DNA. Zoey and her Beast Bot, Jax, make perfect partners. Circle 8 differences between the pictures.

Zoey's energy stores are running low after a tough battle.
Circle half of the carrots in the crate to give her a healthy snack.

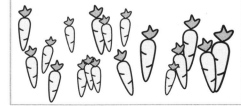

How many carrots does Zoey need to restore her energy?

**4**        **6**        **8**        **9**

# COMBINING FORCES

When the Red, Yellow and Blue Power Rangers' Zords join forces, they can create a vehicle with three times the strength. Rearrange the letters below, using each letter only once, to reveal the name of this moving mecha.

D A G Z R E M O

---

*Now make ten more words of four letters or more using any of the letters above only once.*

**1** _____   **2** _____   **3** _____   **4** _____

**5** _____   **6** _____   **7** _____   **8** _____

**9** _____   **10** _____

# MORPH-X MAZE

The secret agency, Grid Battleforce, combined a special substance with animal DNA to create the Power Rangers Beast Morphers team. Test your navigation skills by completing this maze without lifting your pen from the paper.

START

**Bonus!** Name Grid Battleforce's leader below:

FINISH

# DANGER RANGER

Blaze is under the control of a computer virus and is feeling pretty mixed up – can you help him recover? Place the letters of his name – B, L, A, Z and E – once each into every row and column of the puzzle, and so that two identical letters never touch – not even diagonally.

| | A | | E | |
|---|---|---|---|---|
| Z | | | | A |
| | | A | | |
| A | | | | L |
| | B | | A | |

# OVERPOWERED!

Evox's foot soldiers, the Tronics, appear to be multiplying!
How many enemy fighters can you count altogether?

*Tick the box with the correct number.*

**23**       **27**       **29**

# RANGER IN WAITING

DIFFICULTY:

Once a member of Grid Battleforce, this person was all set to become a Ranger until they became infected by an evil virus! Solve the riddle to work out who it was.

My first letter is in **FABLE** but never in **LEAF.**

My second letter is in **LAB** as well as **RELIEF.**

My third letter is in **BATTLE** but never in **BOTTLE.**

My fourth letter is in **ZORD** but never in **SWORD.**

My fifth letter is in **EVOX** and also in **FOE.**

When you've solved the riddle, write the word below:

------  ------  ------  ------  ------

# BEAST POWER

Finish drawing the other half of these Beast Bot badges to earn your stripes.

# SCREEN SCRAMBLE

Help computer whizz Devon crack the codes by making the mathematical connections with the numbers before and after. The first one has been done for you — the difference between the numbers is three each time.

*Example solution:*

$$3 \, ^{+3} \, 6 \, ^{+3} \, 9 \, ^{+3} \, 12 \, ^{+3} \, 15 \, ^{+3} \, 18 \quad (21)$$

**1** 3  7  11  15  19  23

**2** 2  4  8  14  22  32

**3** 1  2  4  8  16  32

**4** 5  10  20  40  80  160

**5** 121  110  99  88  77  66

# EVIL UPGRADE

Join the dots in numerical order to reveal
a villain whose evil plan is to destroy the
Power Rangers, once and for all.

# MISSING IN ACTION

Go, go, Ranger! Look carefully at the close-ups, then fill in the missing letters to complete the names of five fearless characters.

**1** _ _ X _

**2** _ A _

**3** _ V _ _

**4** _ _ _ _ E

**5** _ T _ _

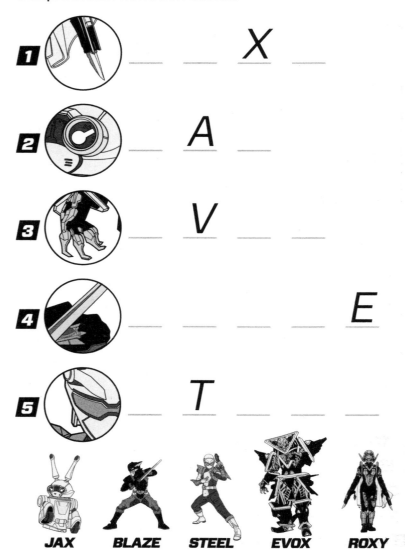

JAX    BLAZE    STEEL    EVOX    ROXY

# MORPHIN MEMORY GAME

How sharp is your memory? Study the picture for 30 seconds before answering the questions about it — without peeking!

**1** Which hand is the Yellow Ranger holding up? ‑‑‑‑‑‑‑‑‑‑

**2** Which enemy is the Blue Ranger taking on? ‑‑‑‑‑‑‑‑‑‑

**3** Which Ranger's Beast Bot is in the picture? ‑‑‑‑‑‑‑‑‑‑

**4** What is the Red Ranger holding? ‑‑‑‑‑‑‑‑‑‑

**5** Are Evil General Roxy's arms up or down? ‑‑‑‑‑‑‑‑‑‑

# CIRCUIT PUZZLE

Trace a path through the circuit below collecting the number codes as you go.

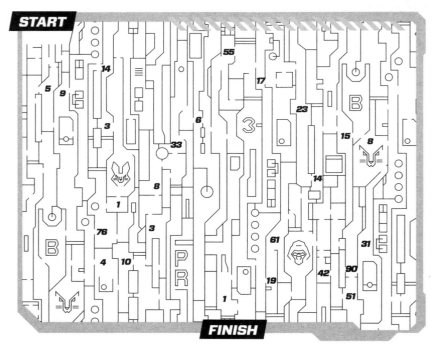

Now fill in the numbers that you have collected below.

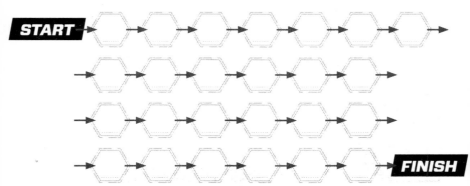

# DOUBLING UP

The Red and Blue Rangers are teaming up for twice the beast power! Can you piece the picture back together in the correct order? Number 1 has been filled in for you.

# ODD WORD OUT

In each of these lines, one of the four words does not belong with the other three. Which word is the odd one out? Work out what the other words have in common.

**1** A. SILVER     B. YELLOW     C. RED     D. BLUE

**2** A. CHEETAH     B. SHARK     C. JACKRABBIT     D. GORILLA

**3** A. NATE     B. STEEL     C. DEVON     D. ZOEY

**4** A. DEFEND     B. BATTLE     C. FIGHT     D. ATTACK

**5** A. KEYBOARD     B. SCREEN     C. MOUSE     D. VIRUS

**6** A. COMMANDER     B. GENERAL     C. PRIVATE     D. LORD

# SMOOTH MOVE

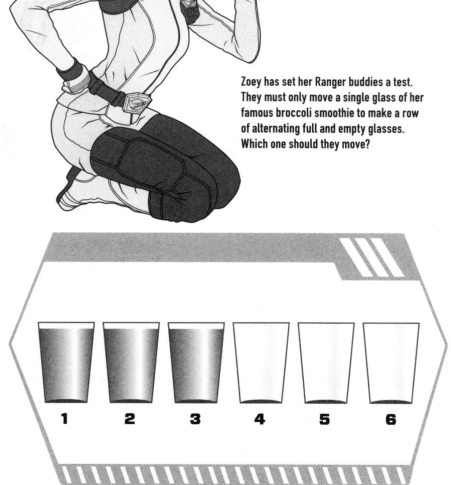

Zoey has set her Ranger buddies a test. They must only move a single glass of her famous broccoli smoothie to make a row of alternating full and empty glasses. Which one should they move?

1   2   3   4   5   6

# WHO'S WHO?

The Power Rangers' bring their different talents to a team that is not afraid to take on the mightiest of villains. Work out who's who from the descriptions.

**1** A Ranger who acts first and asks questions later. A top gamer, prankster and computer hacker.

**2** Stubborn, loyal and as strong as an ox, this Ranger makes a brilliant brother.

**3** A hard worker with a soft spot for Roxy, this Ranger always gives 100%.

**4** This animal-loving, super healthy Ranger is always looking to make the world a better place.

**5** A super-smart Ranger and inventor who built the Rangers' Zords and Beast Bots himself.

# CYBER ATTACK

DIFFICULTY:

Grid Battleforce's systems are temporarily down, due to Evox's vicious virus. To communicate with the Rangers, Commander Shaw has gone old school and sent them a letter.

Before you can open it, trace over the envelope below without:

- lifting your pen from the paper
- crossing any of your lines
- tracing over another line

Practise using a pencil first!

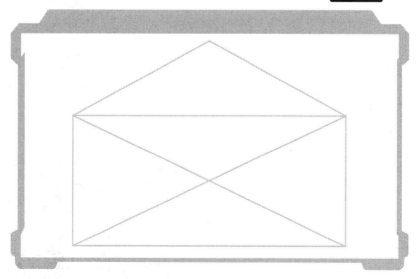

# NEED FOR SPEED

DIFFICULTY:

Commander Shaw and Ravi are assessing the Beast Bots' speed in a test race. The three Beast Bots were tested — Cruise, Smash and Jax.

Commander Shaw says that Smash came first and Jax came second. Ravi says Cruise came first and Smash came second. Neither of them are completely correct — each of them has got one Beast Bot right and one Beast Bot wrong.

*Who really came first, second and third?*

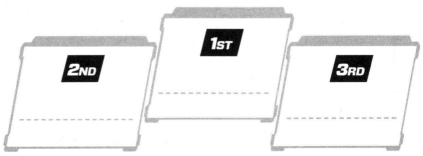

**2ND**

**1ST**

**3RD**

# THRILLS AND DRILLS

After battling the Rangers in the park, Roxy and Drillton have made their escape by burrowing underground. Help the Rangers catch up with the criminals by following them through the tunnel maze.

**START**

**FINISH**

# QUALITY TEAM

DIFFICULTY: 🔧🔧🔧

When putting together its team of Power Rangers, Grid Battleforce selected only the best of the best! Unscramble the words to discover the qualities that each Ranger must possess. The first one has been done for you.

## GRID BATTLEFORCE
### SELECTION PROCESS

**1** HEYTONS     H O N E S T Y ✓

**2** RAYVERB     _ _ _ _ _ _ _ ✓

**3** AGOCURE     _ _ _ _ _ _ _ _ _ ✓

**4** DEPES     _ _ _ _ _ ✓

**5** THERTSGN     _ _ _ _ _ _ _ _ ✓

**6** ALLYTOY     _ _ _ _ _ _ _ ✓

**7** ILLSK     _ _ _ _ _ ✓

**8** NESTIFS     _ _ _ _ _ _ _ ✓

# IN PIECES

Zoey wants to keep her feelings for Nate under wraps — she'd cringe if anyone found out! She has ripped up the pages in her diary to keep things secret. Connect the matching shapes together to stick seven pages back together.

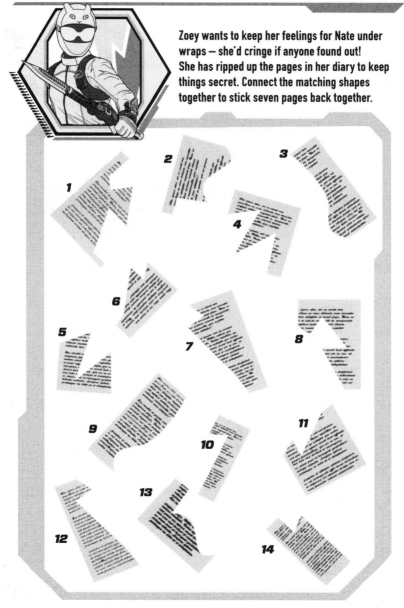

63

# NATE'S NUMBER PUZZLES

Nate is puzzling over how to reprogramme the Beast Bots.
Help him fill in the blanks to get Cruise, Smash and
Jax functioning again.

## Rules

**1.** Each column and row must contain
the numbers 1–4 only once.

**2.** The same number immediately next
to or below each other is not allowed.

## Puzzle 1: *CRUISE*

| | | | |
|---|---|---|---|
| 3 | | | 2 |
| | 4 | 1 | |
| | 3 | 2 | |
| 4 | | | 1 |

## Puzzle 2: SMASH

## Puzzle 3: JAX

# ANSWERS
## CHECK HOW YOU SCORED!

# ZORD ORDER

**ZORD**
▼
**WORD**
▼
**WOOD**
▼
**GOOD**

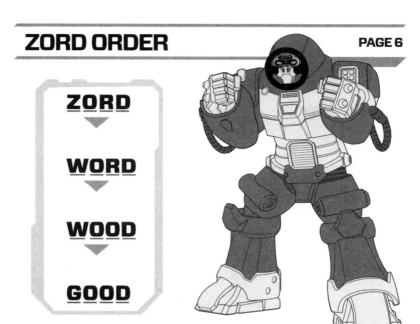

# REAL RANGER

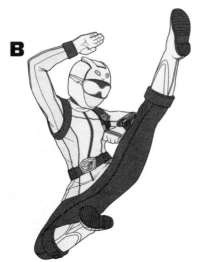

**B**

The Real Ranger is Ranger B.

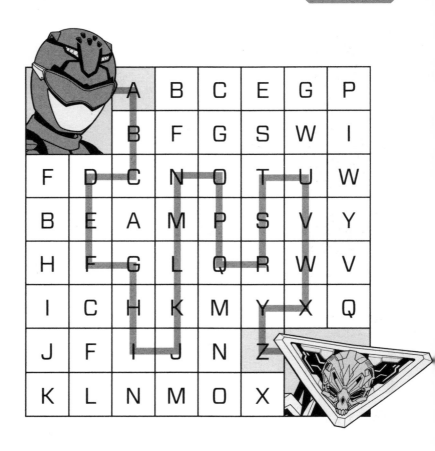

| | A | B | C | E | G | P |
|---|---|---|---|---|---|---|
| | B | F | G | S | W | I |
| F | D | C | N | O | T | U | W |
| B | E | A | M | P | S | V | Y |
| H | F | G | L | Q | R | W | V |
| I | C | H | K | M | Y | X | Q |
| J | F | I | J | N | Z | | |
| K | L | N | M | O | X | | |

The answer is:

*R A N G E R S*

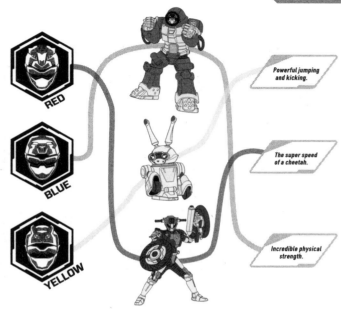

Powerful jumping and kicking.

The super speed of a cheetah.

Incredible physical strength.

## *Quick Count*
The word DNA is spelled seven times.

# BATTLE SCARS

PAGE 11

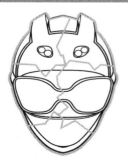

THE POWER RANGERS MUST TRAVEL INTO
THE CYBER DIMENSION TO DEFEAT EVOX.

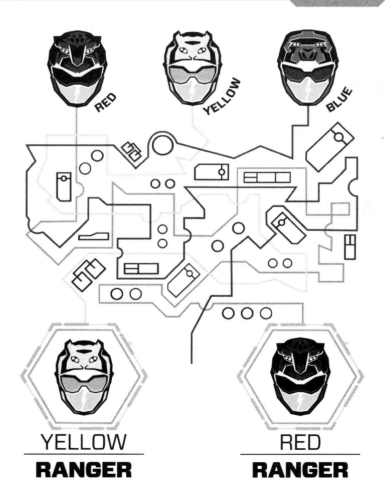

YELLOW
**RANGER**

RED
**RANGER**

# TEAM TEST

RED
**1** NEVDO
*DEVON*

BLUE
**2** IVAR
*RAVI*

YELLOW
**3** OYEZ
*ZOEY*

GOLD
**4** ETAN
*NATE*

## Quick Quiz
1. *ZOEY*
2. *DEVON*
3. *NATE*
4. *RAVI*

# SMASH AND GRAB

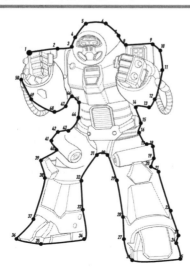

## Name That Mecha: *SMASH*

# ON THE ROX

PAGE 16

### Puzzle 1: Easy

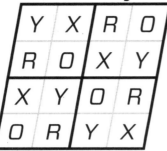

| Y | X | R | O |
|---|---|---|---|
| R | O | X | Y |
| X | Y | O | R |
| O | R | Y | X |

### Puzzle 2: Medium

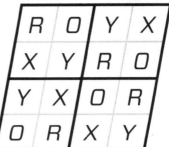

| R | O | Y | X |
|---|---|---|---|
| X | Y | R | O |
| Y | X | O | R |
| O | R | X | Y |

# EVOX'S EVOLUTION

PAGE 18

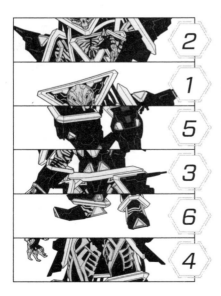

2
1
5
3
6
4

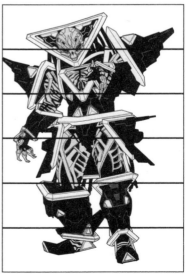

## BUILDING A BROTHER

PAGE 17

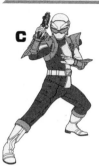

C

Robot C is the finished Steel.

## MECH MAZE

PAGE 19

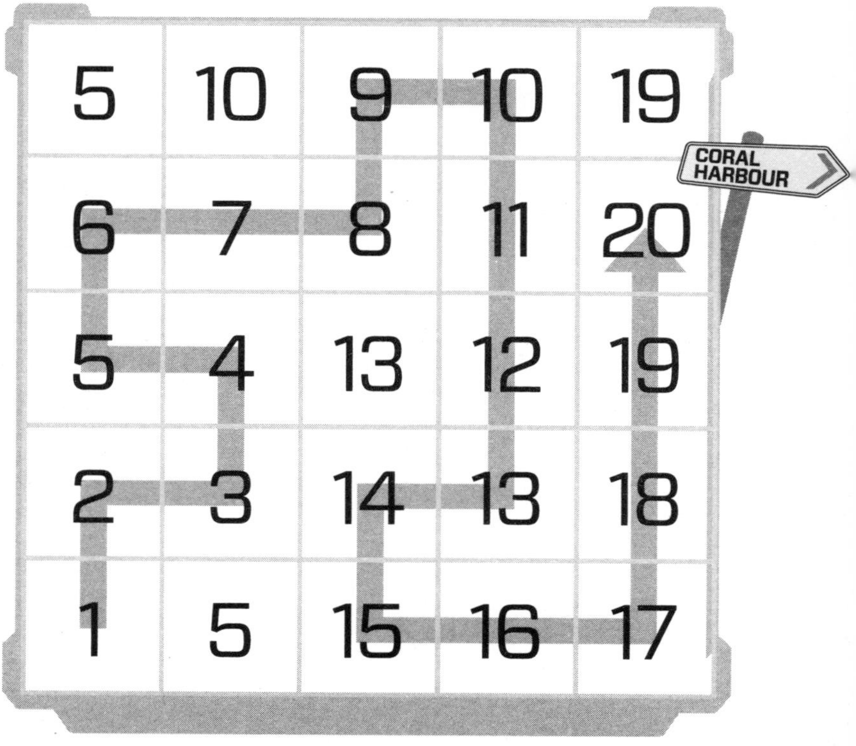

5 10 9 10 19
6 7 8 11 20
5 4 13 12 19
2 3 14 13 18
1 5 15 16 17
CORAL HARBOUR

# GOING VIRAL

**PAGE 20**

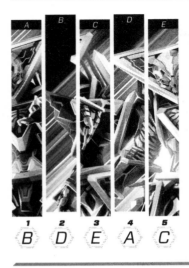

**1** B **2** D **3** E **4** A **5** C

# VILE VILLAINS

**PAGE 21**

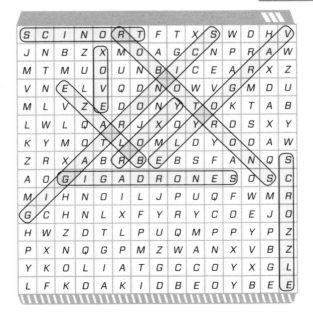

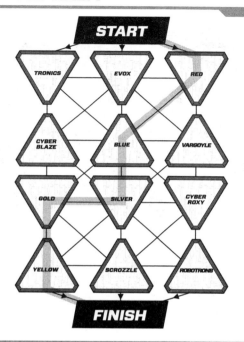

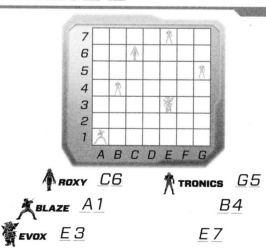

ROXY *C6*  TRONICS *G5*

BLAZE *A1*  *B4*

EVOX *E3*  *E7*

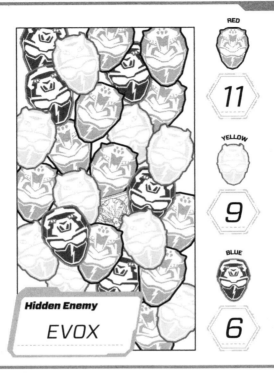

RED

**11**

YELLOW

**9**

BLUE

**6**

**Hidden Enemy**

*EVOX*

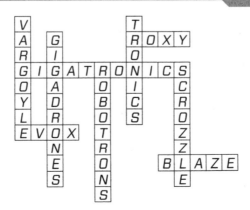

# TOUGH WORKOUT

**PAGE 26**

## SAY CHEESE!

**PAGE 27**

Devon's message is:

XXSTXAXNXDBXAXCXKX

**STAND BACK**

XIXXMXGXOXNXNXA

**I'M GONNA**

XMXOXRXPXHX!

**MORPH!**

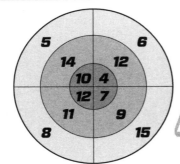

5 + 9 + 4

5 + 12 + 4

15 + 14 + 12

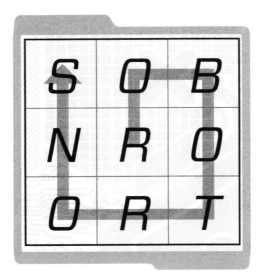

The nine-letter word for the mystery monsters is ROBOTRONS.

Some five-letter words include: boron, boost, robot, roost, roots, rotor, snoot, toons and torso.

# FORCE FOR GOOD

***Which Rangers?*** The Rangers featured are the Blue, Red and Yellow Rangers.

# ZORD LAUNCH

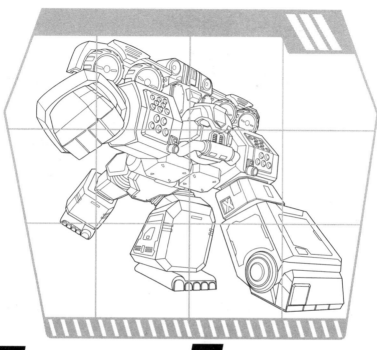

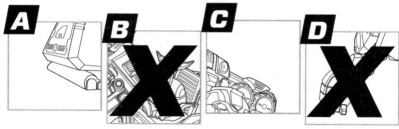

**Which Mode?** In which mode is the Zord shown above?

CAR ☐   CHEETAH ☐   BATTLE ✓

```
      Y
  R E D
  B L U E
S I L V E R
  G O L D
      W
```

## OUT OF SEQUENCE

**1**

**2**

**3**

**4**

# RELEASE THE BEASTS!

PAGE 37

**1 STAG BEETLE**

**GORILLA 2**

**3 JACKRABBIT**

# BLADE BUILDER

PAGE 38

The answer is YELLOW.

The number of triangles forms of 1 unit: 16
The number of triangles forms of 4 units: 7
The number of triangles forms of 9 units: 3
The number of triangles forms of 19 units: 1
The answer is **27 triangles**.

**9** carrots. ✓

## COMBINING FORCES

**PAGE 44**

The mecha is: ***MEGAZORD***

Some of the words that can be made include:

maze(d), mazer, gazer, gaze(d), graze, adoze, doze(r), raze(d), dogma, gamed, game(r), marge, omega, armed, derma, dream, drome, gored, grade, raged, adore, oared, daze, zero, game, germ, gorm, gram, mage, dame, demo, dome, dorm, dram, made, mead, mode, aged, drag, dreg, egad, goad, grad, mare, more, ream, rome, ager, ergo, gear, goer, gore, ogre, rage, dare, dear, doer, read, redo, road, rode, aero, agro.

# MORPH-X MAZE

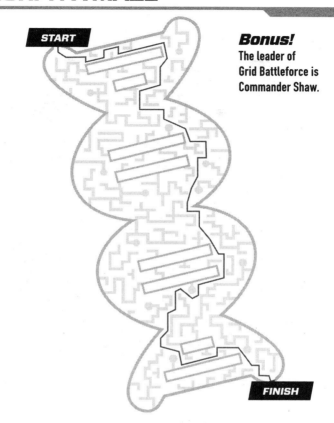

**START**

**_Bonus!_**
The leader of
Grid Battleforce is
Commander Shaw.

**FINISH**

# DANGER RANGER

| L | A | Z | E | B |
| Z | E | B | L | A |
| B | L | A | Z | E |
| A | Z | E | B | L |
| E | B | L | A | Z |

There are **27** foot soldiers.

## RANGER IN WAITING

PAGE 48

*The answer is:*

B L A Z E

## SCREEN SCRAMBLE

PAGE 50

**1.** 27; **2.** 44; **3.** 64; **4.** 320; **5.** 55.

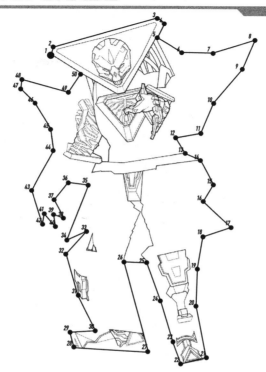

**1** ROXY

**2** JAX

**3** EVOX

**4 5** BLAZE STEEL

# MORPHIN MEMORY GAME

PAGE 53

**1.** right; **2.** Evil General Blaze; **3.** the Red Rangers' – Cruise;
**4.** his Beast-X blade; **5.** down.

# CIRCUIT PUZZLE

PAGE 54

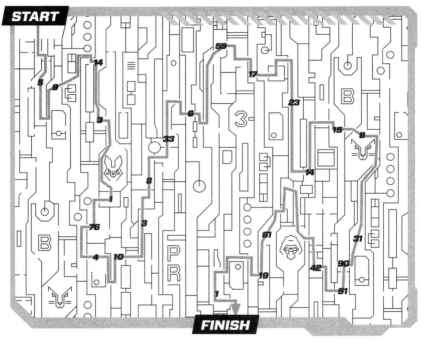

**START** ➤ 5 ➤ 9 ➤ 14 ➤ 3 ➤ 1 ➤ 76 ➤ 4 ➤

➤ 10 ➤ 3 ➤ 8 ➤ 33 ➤ 6 ➤ 55 ➤

➤ 17 ➤ 23 ➤ 14 ➤ 15 ➤ 8 ➤ 31 ➤

➤ 90 ➤ 51 ➤ 42 ➤ 61 ➤ 19 ➤ 1 ➤ **FINISH**

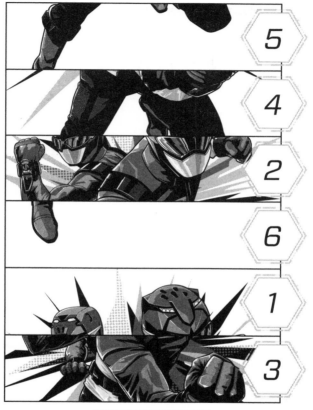

5

4

2

6

1

3

# ODD WORD OUT

PAGE 56

**1.** A – silver (the other Rangers are primary colours)
**2.** B – shark (the others are Beast Bot forms)
**3.** B – Steel (the others are all human)
**4.** A – defend (the others are all offensive words)
**5.** D – virus (the others are all computer hardware parts)
**6.** D – lord (the others are all army ranks)

# SMOOTH MOVE

PAGE 57

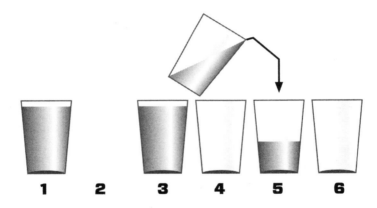

1    2    3    4    5    6

The Rangers should pour the smoothie in glass 2 into glass 5.

# WHO'S WHO?

PAGE 58

**1.** Red Ranger; **2.** Silver Ranger; **3.** Blue Ranger;
**4.** Yellow Ranger; **5.** Gold Ranger.

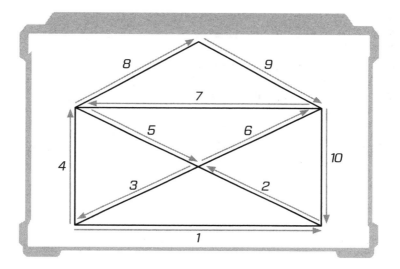

If Commander Shaw is right about Smash coming first, then she must be wrong about Jax coming second, and so the real order would be:

**1.** Smash          **2.** Cruise,          **3.** Jax.

If Commander Shaw is wrong about Smash coming first, then she must be right about Jax coming second, and so the real order would be:

**1.** Cruise          **2.** Jax,          **3.** Smash.

If Ravi is right about Cruise coming first, then he must be wrong about Crush coming second, and so the real order would be:

**1.** Cruise,          **2.** Jax,          **3.** Smash.

If Ravi is wrong about Cruise coming first, then he must be right about Crush coming second, and so the real order would be:

**1.** Jax,          **2.** Smash,          **3.** Jax.

The answer must be the two orders that agree: **1.** Cruise; **2.** Jax; **3.** Smash.

# THRILLS AND DRILLS

START

FINISH

# QUALITY TEAM

PAGE 62

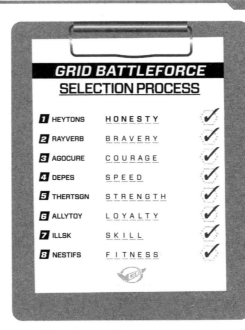

### GRID BATTLEFORCE
### SELECTION PROCESS

**1** HEYTONS    H O N E S T Y ✓

**2** RAYVERB    B R A V E R Y ✓

**3** AGOCURE    C O U R A G E ✓

**4** DEPES    S P E E D ✓

**5** THERTSGN    S T R E N G T H ✓

**6** ALLYTOY    L O Y A L T Y ✓

**7** ILLSK    S K I L L ✓

**8** NESTIFS    F I T N E S S ✓

94

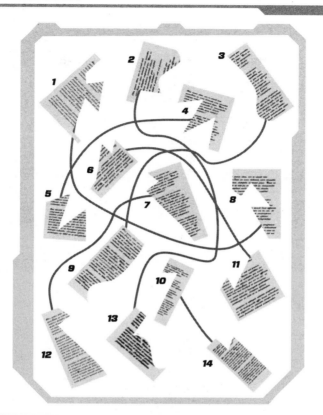

## NATE'S NUMBER PUZZLES  PAGES 64–65

**Puzzle 1: CRUISE**

| 3 | 1 | 4 | 2 |
| 2 | 4 | 1 | 3 |
| 1 | 3 | 2 | 4 |
| 4 | 2 | 3 | 1 |

**Puzzle 2: SMASH**

| 4 | 1 | 2 | 3 |
| 2 | 3 | 4 | 1 |
| 3 | 4 | 1 | 2 |
| 1 | 2 | 3 | 4 |

**Puzzle 3: JAX**

| 2 | 4 | 3 | 1 |
| 3 | 1 | 4 | 2 |
| 1 | 3 | 2 | 4 |
| 4 | 2 | 1 | 3 |